BLUE
Penguins, Bells and Open Skies

Even more imaginative relaxations
for lively kids

MARIA OLIVER

ISBN: 978-1-8383024-7-4

DEDICATION

To the following superstar children and their fabulous grown-ups:
Aadhya, Andrew, Colby, Evaine, Gladys, Iris, Isla, Jasmine, Logan,
Lucas, Penny, Scarlett and Seren.
Thanks to Jack and Lily the cats. Not only are you great models, but you purr beautifully
and headbutt me nicely when I'm trying to type. Any mistakes are down to you.

Thanks for the love and encouragement from:
Andrew, Lucas and Seren
Rachel and Dennis
Ben and Steph.

.

CONTENTS

FOREWORD

This collection of relaxing stories is a mixture. Some are inspired by being out in nature in my native England, as in my previous two books. But two are from the other side of the world! It's many years since I travelled to New Zealand, but some of the experiences left a strong impression on me, so I returned there in my imagination for two of these stories.

Some were improvised when teaching a themed children's yoga class, and can be used at specific times of year – such as on Pancake Day, Hallowe'en or World Book Day. The Skeleton illustration is based on my foam jigsaw skeleton, Gladys, who helps me in my children's yoga classes. (Gladys was named after a class member's pet hamster!)

Some, like 'Golden Ball of Energy' and 'Windscreen Wipers' are my take on Yoga Philosophy, and the idea that energy, or Prana, flows through us and all living things. Whatever you believe, the idea of Prana flowing through invisible channels known as Nadis, and whirling round invisible wheels known as Chakras, is a fascinating way of thinking about our bodies.

All of these stories have the same aim: to get people of all ages to tune into their bodies and their breath, put aside everyday worries and find inner calm just for a short while. I hope they leave you and the people in your life feeling refreshed and re-energised.

ဆ

"Children won't lie still"

That's
what some
-one told me.
Here are all the
clever things
I wish I'd
said in
reply. Adults find
it hard to be still too.
Everyone needs a little help to be
calm and quiet. That's why my books
help. I didn't tell them about the rooms
full of children I have taught lying quietly,
maybe fidgeting a little, maybe giggling a
little, but mostly lying still, calm, quiet.
It's hard not to be distracted – I wrote
Gingerbread Biscuits, so that children
would   lie a little distance away   from
each   other and not tickle or   giggle
at each   other. It's hard not to   fidget;
that's   why I wrote *Skeleton*, so   that
children   would be motivated not to   move,
and why   I wrote *Windscreen Wipers*   so that
children   would be able to move,   but in a
purposeful way. It's hard to be still for a long time – that's why some of
these relaxations are short. It's hard to lie still and do nothing – that's why
these relaxations take you on an adventure in your imagination
and make you want to listen to find out what happens next.
Relaxing can be hard, but these stories make it easier.
Maybe the person meant "I haven't seen children lying still *yet*."

෨෬

1. Skeleton

Imagine that you are just a skeleton. You have no muscles, so you lie as still as you can.

But of course, you are allowed to breathe! Breathe slowly, and let your bones rest.

Your body is only made of bones, lying heavily on the floor. You feel so heavy, lying so still.

Your face is completely still.

Your arms and legs are still.

Your fingers and toes… so still.

No muscle, so your bones cannot move.

Just lying heavily, maybe sinking slightly into the floor, breathing slowly, feeling so heavy and so still.

So heavy… and so still…

When you are ready to move, imagine that you have muscles only in your fingers and give them a wiggle. Now you have muscles in your toes as well. Now muscles in your arms… and your legs… in your neck… now you can sit up and stretch!

Do you find it hard to lie still, or does it make you worried? Try jumping about like crazy until you get out of breath, then try lying down again like a skeleton!

ಭಚ

2. You are a Flying Insect

You're lying in a garden on the grass on a warm, lazy day. There are flowers of all colours and sizes around you; every time you breathe in you smell something different. There is buzzing and fluttering all around, and you start to notice insects of different shapes, colours and sizes. They are all friendly insects of the kind you like best.

You decide that you'd like to be an insect. Are you a brightly coloured butterfly, with big, floaty wings? A bee, or a fly with buzzing wings? Or a dragonfly with sparkling wings? Choose an insect that flies and find yourself shrinking, hovering in the air.

The gentle breeze wafts you around and brings fabulous smells straight to you. Your insect eyes now see glowing colours on all the flowers, which guide you to the best smells. Look at the bright colours below you, you can imagine the most fantastical colours on these flowers because you are seeing them through your super insect eyes.

What smells do you smell? They can be any smells you like, not just flower smells. Chocolate cake, toast, strawberry jam… any of the smells that you like are floating towards you.

One flower in particular is so big and inviting that you have to fly over. The smell is the best smell in the world and the petals are all your favourite colours at once. Fly down deep into the flower. Your long insect tongue pokes out and drinks the flower's nectar, which tastes of your favourite drink.

You feel full and happy, so you decide to rest inside the flower. The sun shines through the petals and fills the flower with glowing coloured light.

You are surrounded by glowing colour and your favourite smell, and you still taste your favourite drink. The petals are like soft sheets and you feel safe and supported. Around you is the buzz of other friendly insects, flying and fluttering between the flowers.

ೞಂಶ

Inspired after doing a children's yoga class based on *The Very Hungry Caterpillar* by Eric Carle.

3. A Paper Bag on a Windy Day

If you were a paper bag, what colour would you be? Brown or white? Patterned or plain?

Imagine you are a paper bag lying on the ground outside. The wind begins to blow, gently at first, so that you lift up slightly at the edges. Then more strongly so that you are raised high in the air.

The wind seems to be playing a game with you. Sometimes you are lifted up high, sometimes you are lowered down again. Sometimes you turn over and over and over, head over heels, or round and round like a spinning top.

The wind is friendly and can tell what you'd like it to do. You can drift lazily, blown along gently, looking down at everything going on beneath you. Or you can be thrown around roughly, high up and then dropping suddenly until you almost reach the ground.

What can you see around you? Do you find yourself blown as high as the tops of the trees? How far away can you see? Are there people below, watching you getting blown about?

When you are ready, the wind lowers you gently to the ground, where you land gently and rest.

છ૭લ્ર

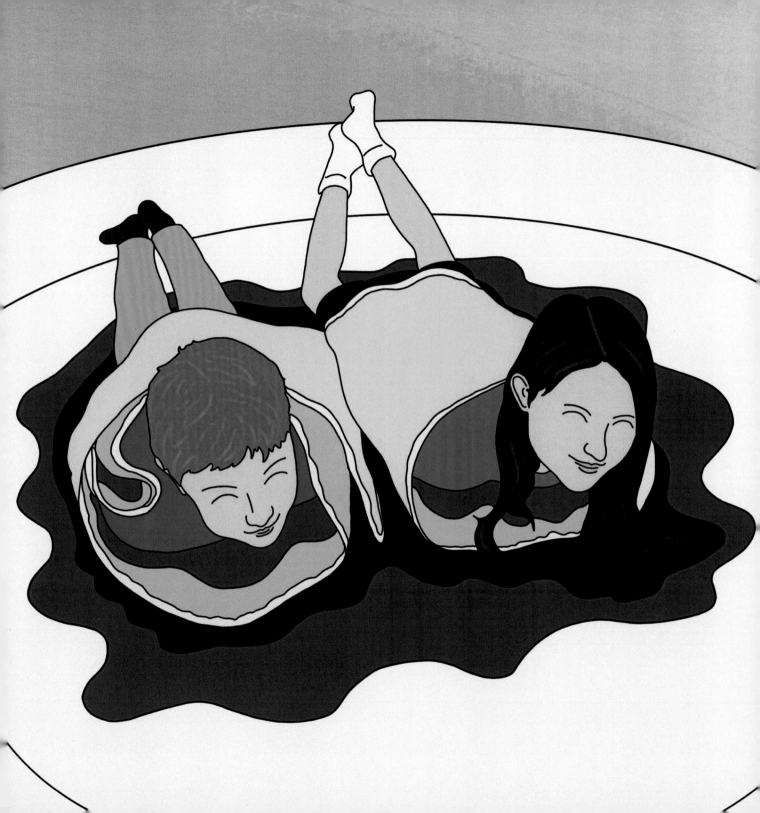

4. You are lying on a Pancake

Imagine lying on a warm pancake, which has just come out of the frying pan. It is spread with your favourite pancake filling.

Is it gooey chocolate spread?

Crunchy sugar and sticky lemon juice?

Jam, cream, or marshmallows?

Fruit and melted chocolate?

You lie on the warm pancake and feel the filling against your skin. Can you smell it when you breathe in?

Now imagine that the pancake is being rolled up with you inside.

If you're on a yoga mat, blanket or rug, you can roll the sides up around you.

You're surrounded by warm, crispy pancake. You feel safe and comfortable, and the amazing smell is all around you. Lie still for as long as you want.

෨෬

5. You are a Gingerbread Biscuit

Have you ever made gingerbread people? Lie flat in the shape of a gingerbread person. Flat on your back, arms a little away from your body and feet apart. If your hair is in a pony-tail, lie with your head to one side.

When you bake biscuits and cookies you have to make sure that they don't touch each other on the baking tray. This is because they might spread out in the oven and stick together. So if you are in a room with other people, make sure that you are not touching anyone else.

Close your eyes and imagine that your baking tray is being lifted up and put into an oven. In real life we would never put ourselves in an oven because it would be too hot. But because we are gingerbread people the oven feels just right to us.

When we are in the oven we feel cosy and warm and soft and squishy. We melt a little and spread out a bit more along the baking tray.

Lie there enjoying the warm feeling, imagining yourself spreading out more and more as you bake. When you breathe in, imagine smelling the amazing gingerbread smell. If you don't like gingerbread, it can be any cookie flavour smell that you like.

If you are doing this in a class, maybe your teacher can ring a bell or singing bowl and pretend that this is the timer on the oven saying that you are fully baked! Imagine being lifted out of the oven and starting to cool down. Give your fingers and toes a wriggle, stretch and sit up.

හ⭗ශ

6. Sunflower Field

Imagine standing before a field of sunflowers, stretching tall above you. The sun is high in the perfect blue sky, and all the flowers are turning their faces upwards and to the same side. Walk along the edge of this field of sunflowers. You notice a gap in between some of the stalks, and you see that it is the start of an inviting, exciting path.

Step in between the sunflower stalks and follow this path. It is cool in between the green stalks, and they rustle as you brush past them. The ground is hard and dusty, as if it hasn't rained for a long time. Maybe you are wearing shoes, or maybe you are barefoot so you can feel the earth against the soles of your feet.

Carry on along the path between the sunflowers. When you look up, you see the green undersides of the flowers with the blue sky glowing in between. One sunflower stalk is swaying from side to side, and a beautiful, merry trilling sound is coming from its top. The trilling gets louder the closer you get. The sunflower gives a final shake and through the gaps in the flower heads, you see a small, brown bird taking off – it is a nightingale.

Would you like to follow the nightingale? Imagine shrinking and floating off the dusty ground, so that you drift through a gap in between the sunflowers and into the dazzling sunshine. Float above sunflowers, stretching golden yellow to the horizon, where they meet the deep blue sky. Sunflower after sunflower, all turning the same way, gently swaying in the breeze. You almost believe that you are floating above a golden sea.

Insects are buzzing in and out of the sunflower heads, filling the air with their humming and buzzing. You twist and turn in mid-air to spot the nightingale, feeling the sun shining on you and gazing up at the beautiful blue, cloudless sky, before twisting back down to gaze at the golden sunflowers.

The happy trilling sound pierces above the insects' buzzing and you turn to see the nightingale perched on another sunflower, not far away. Float towards the nightingale, and see it take off again, leaving the sunflower shaking beneath it. It flies to another sunflower, sings, and then takes off again when you get closer.

This time the nightingale soars up higher into the sky, fluttering its wings rapidly and then gliding. Follow the nightingale higher, up towards the blue sky, then back down again towards the sea of sunflowers.

The nightingale lands on another sunflower, and you decide that you'd like to rest. Shrink even smaller so that you can curl up inside one of the sunflowers, against its seeds. The nightingale stays on its sunflower nearby, trilling contentedly, and you gaze up at the blue sky, framed by golden petals.

ഇൽ

Sunflowers turn their faces to the sun and follow it across the sky each day, until they are fully grown, when they stay fixed towards the east and the rising sun.

It is not true that sunflowers turn to face each other on cloudy days. But we can.

The sunflower is the national flower of Ukraine. They grow in fields so that the seeds can be made into Sunflower Oil.

The Ukrainian Flag is yellow and blue. The blue represents the sky, and the yellow the fertile ground where their crops grow.

The national bird of Ukraine is the Nightingale.

This relaxation was written to send to Ukrainian children.

7. Floating into a Book

Do you have a favourite sort of book? Do you like books with pictures, or mainly words? Books about animals, monsters, adventures, magic, different places?

Let's imagine floating into our favourite books.

Imagine your book laid open on the floor in front of you. Maybe it's open on one of your favourite pages, where the best bits happen. You find yourself shrinking, pulled towards the book. Landing on its pages, you hear the rustle and smell the smell of the paper… then you find yourself inside the book.

Maybe you have floated into one of the pictures, or maybe you are in a scene described by the words in the book. You are invisible, and nobody can hear you either.

What can you see?

Are your favourite characters talking or arguing? Is there a building, or mountains? Is there food to smell? Are you indoors by the fire, or outside in the wind? Wherever you are, imagine yourself floating up high. If you're inside, you can float out through a door, a window, an archway, a cave entrance… if you're outside just keep floating. Look down at the story getting smaller and smaller as you float higher. Buildings, mountains, animals, magical creatures, all getting smaller as you float further away.

You smell paper again and realise that you are floating out of your book, and back to where you started. Lie still for a while, thinking about where you have been.

ༀ

Written for World Book Week

8. Glowing Bluebells

You're walking along a lane and it's just starting to get dark. There are trees either side of the lane, branches stretching up and meeting overhead. A wooden fence runs along one side, and you reach a small gate. A blue glow is coming from over the fence. Look over the top of the gate and into the trees.

Through the gate is a wood. The trees are tall with pale green leaves, and the ground is glowing blue. The light is fading, but the blue glow becomes brighter. Open the gate and walk into the wood, closing the gate carefully behind you.

The blue glow is interrupted by earthy paths which are soft under your feet. Walk towards the nearest patch of glowing blue. The blue glow comes from thousands of bluebells, packed in tightly together. When you look closely, you see that they are not all exactly the same shade of blue. Some bluebells have purple shading, some are paler. Some bluebells are white, some are pink. But most of all, the ground glows blue in between the trees, stretching back as far as you can see.

It seems to have become darker, but the bluebells glow even more brightly. Birds are flitting from one tree to another, and singing high up in their branches; a night-time song before the day ends.

Follow a path through the bluebells. It comes to a dead end, but the ground looks comfortable, dry and soft. Lie down on the path, bluebells either side of you and around your head. You can see the blue glow around you and above your head. Breathe in a lungful of sweet bluebell scent, as if you are breathing in the blue glow. Breathing out, feel safe, calm and protected in this quiet wood, listening to the birds and surrounded by the blue glow.

ஐௐ

9. Golden Ball of Energy

Use this if you need energy, or if you have a big worry that you need to do something about.

Imagine that inside you, above your belly button, there is a fire.

It's in the place that we call our energy centre. Another name is the Solar Plexus, which is a bundle of important nerves that meet in the energy centre and make the shape of a sun.

Solar means sun, and the sun is a ball of brightly burning flame. Yogis call the flame inside us the Agni, or inner flame. They believe it gives us energy, and burns what we don't need, like worries or fears.

Lie down and imagine a ball of flame inside you, at your energy centre. How big is it? Is it bright, or dull?

Keep your breathing slow and relaxed. When you breathe in, let your belly lift up so that your breath goes to your flame. When you breathe out, let your belly flop down again.

Every time you breathe in, imagine your flame getting bigger and brighter.

What can you use your flame to get rid of? If you are worried about something, think of what the worry looks like. Imagine throwing the worry into the flame and watching it burn away.

The bigger the flame gets, the stronger and more full of energy you feel. The flame gives off a bright, golden-yellow light. Imagine the light spreading from your energy centre all the way through you, down your legs to your toes, up to your chest and up to the top of your head, and down your arms to your fingers.

You are full of energy and glowing all over with warm, golden-yellow light.

You might also want to say a positive affirmation to yourself, to really make yourself feel strong. Choose one that works for you, such as…

I am strong

I can do this

I feel brave

I have energy.

ഇരു

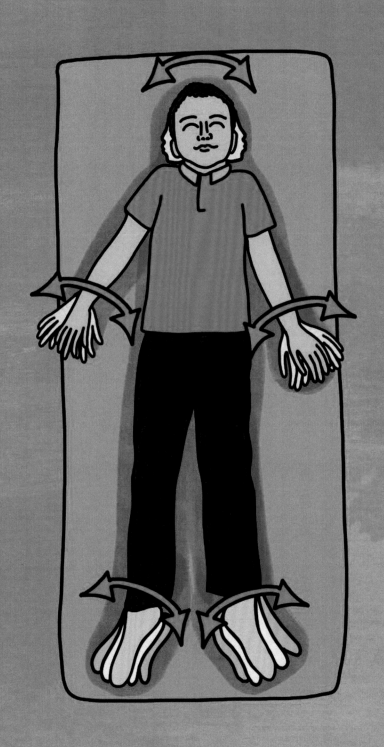

10. Windscreen Wipers

People who do yoga like to think of energy as something that flows through you – not just through your blood and nerves, but all the way through and out into the world around you!

They believe that if we feel tired or upset, it may be because our energy is blocked somewhere inside us. This exercise is called Kaya Kriya and is supposed to clear out your flow of energy so that you feel relaxed, but also ready for anything! You need to concentrate on moving at the same time as you breathe, so it can stop unhelpful thoughts as well.

We're going to imagine that our legs, arms, and head are like windscreen wipers, cleaning out anything we don't need so that we feel fresh and new.

The slower you breathe and move, the cleaner you will feel. But you can try it fast and then slow if you like.

Lie on your back with your legs out straight. Let yourself feel floppy and heavy.

Your feet are the first set of windscreen wipers.

When you breathe in, turn your toes in towards each other, and when you breathe out, let them flop back out again. Breathe in… toes in… breathe out… toes out… Repeat this two or three times.

Now let your feet stay flopped outwards. Your hands are the next set of windscreen wipers.

Lie with your hands towards the floor. When you breathe in, roll your arms outwards so your palms of your hands face the ceiling. When you breathe out, roll them back so that your palms are on the floor again.

Breathe in… palms up… breathe out… palms down… Repeat this two or three times.

Now let your hands rest. Your head is the next windscreen wiper. When you breathe in, roll your head to the right, when you breathe out, roll to the left. Breathe in… roll right… breathe out… roll left… Repeat this two or three times.

You can put all three together if you want! When you breathe in, first move your legs, then arms, then head. When you breathe out, move your legs then arms, then head.

Breathe in… toes in… palms up… head right… breathe out… toes out… palms down… head left…

You can carry on until you just don't feel like moving any more, then lie still for as long as you like.

How do you feel now?

෨෨

11. A Cave of Glow Worms

Glow worms are not really worms! In the UK they are a type of beetle, but in New Zealand, they are the larvae of a fly. This story is all about a cave in New Zealand.

The cave is very dark, but you have a torch. Imagine walking into the cave, right to the back, where there is a tunnel. Follow the tunnel, using your torch to look around. The walls are black rock, and water drips down them, shining in the torchlight. The tunnel goes downhill. Keep following until you reach water.

Floating on the water is a black rubber ring. It is big enough to hold you. Climb onto the rubber ring and lie back. And now… imagine switching off the torch.

Tiny green lights appear above you. The roof of the cave is so high up, and so big, that it's as if you are looking at a sky crowded with green stars.

The rubber ring starts to move and you realise that you are floating on an underground river. Float lazily along, looking up at the green stars. The glow worms are on the roof of the cave above you, and on the walls either side. Sometimes you can see thin strands, like glimmering strings of beads, hanging from the walls and ceiling.

Carry on floating, looking up at millions of tiny points of green light against the black, wet rock of the cave.

Soon the rubber ring comes to a stop. You find you can climb out easily, back onto solid rock. You can see a tunnel leading out of the cave. Choose whether you want to leave the cave or stay floating on the rubber ring, gently rocking, gazing up at the glow worms.

෨൪

12. Forest Bathing

Have you ever heard of Forest Bathing? It means walking in the woods! Being surrounded by green can make you feel calm and relaxed.

Picture a muddy path leading between trees and under branches. It looks so inviting. Step in between the trees and enter the wood.

All the trees look different. White silver birches with black splodges on the trunk, oak trees with twisted branches, horse chestnut trees with five-fingered leaves. Ivy grows up some tree trunks, moss grows up others. It is cool in the wood, under the roof of leaves.

The ground is covered in fern leaves, uncoiling upwards. Holly bushes with shiny, spiky leaves are scattered around. The air smells of green – if you can imagine how green would smell, this is it. Green, clean, damp air from the trees, taking what you breathe out and making it good to breathe in again.

Looking upwards, you see how the sunlight shines through the leaves of the trees. The leaves are almost see-through except where they overlap each other. In between the leaves you can see the blue of the sky.

Do you want to stay on the ground, or climb one of the trees? Imagine a tree with firm branches that you can reach. Feel the rough bark under your fingers as you climb. When you have had enough of climbing, sit on a branch and let the tree hold you.

Look up at the green light shining through the leaves, surrounded by green above you, around you and below. When you look at your skin, it has a faint green glow, as if you are underwater, bathing in the light

ജ

13. Little Blue Fairy Penguins

Blue penguins are also known as Little Blue or Fairy penguins. They live in New Zealand and Australia and are the smallest type of penguin.

All penguins look a bit awkward when they are waddling on land, but when they get in the water, they glide and soar with grace and ease.

Sometimes I feel that things are difficult, and that I have to waddle slowly to sort them out. Sometimes I feel that I am gliding effortlessly and that life is easy.

Imagine that you are on a beach, looking at the sea. You want to get into the sea, but it feels such a long way away. Your feet sink into the sand, your legs are only small so you take small steps. It's so tiring. Then you reach the sea. Waddle out a little way, feeling the waves lapping against you. Take a moment to look at the blue sea, where it meets the blue, cloudless sky. Now, take a deep breath and jump into the air.

You splash gracefully into a wave and dive to the sea bed. How good it feels, to be carried by water, shooting quickly along. Other blue penguins are around you and you see them gliding, bubbles streaming from their beaks and sparkling around them. Maybe you do look a little like magical fairies, darting this way and that in the water, with bubbles glittering all around.

Under the water you can somersault, roll, glide, swim up and dive down again. Shafts of sunlight shine through the clear water and you swim through, or in and out. Soon you decide it's time to go back to shore. Swim to the surface, and float on top of the sea as you paddle your way back.

Once you reach the beach, lie on the sand, letting your feathers dry out in the sun.

80C3

14. You are a Bouncing Conker

Conkers are another name for Horse Chestnuts. They are smooth and shiny, and I love collecting them in Autumn. Sometimes I see them dropping out of trees and bouncing off the ground.

Curl up tight in a ball, and imagine that you are a conker, tucked away in a green, spiky shell. It's warm, dark and cosy, but then you start to feel a cold draught on your back. The draught gets a bit stronger, the light starts to creep in, and your shell doesn't feel quite so cosy any more. You realise that you are ready to burst out of your shell.

The shell is opening up and you can't stay inside any longer. Do you feel you want to cling on, or are you excited about what is waiting for you outside? The shell opens a little more and suddenly, you find yourself dropping out into the world.

The air rushes past you as you whizz to the ground then BOING! You bounce on the ground and rush upwards again!

Turning over and over in the air, you see blue sky above and the green grass below. You slow down in mid-air and then find yourself starting to fall again.

This time you see a pile of soft leaves zooming up to meet you and you land gently; no more bouncing.

Rest in your pile of leaves. Maybe someone will pick you up to take you home, admiring how shiny and magnificent you are. Maybe you will stay where you are and grow into a tree. Right now, you can enjoy being still after your glorious drop to the ground.

ৎ◌ও

15. You are a cat out at night

Do you have a pet cat? Do you sometimes feel that they are not really *your* cat, and that they have a life of their own? My cats often sleep in the house during the day, but sometimes stay out all night. I wonder what they're doing.

At night, the outside world looks completely different. There are different noises, different animals and birds, the stars come out and it feels colder.

Imagine turning into a cat. Grow a thick, glossy coat of fur, which can be any pattern you like. Are you a black cat, a stripey Tabby, a fluffy long-haired cat, or are you a crazy-coloured cat? You can be whatever sort of cat you want.

Imagine going to your door and finding a useful catflap there. Push it open with your nose, and step outside. What is outside your door? Remember that you're closer to the ground, so it looks different now that you're a cat.

Your ears swivel so that you hear noises everywhere. Bats are flitting above you, spiders are pattering across the ground, slugs are munching on leaves, a rustle in a bush might be another cat, or a fox.

Your eyes are sharper, so you can see small movements all around. Moths fluttering against a light, leaves moving in the wind, an owl flying to the branch of a tree.

Your sense of smell is stronger, so you can smell sweet flowers, rubbish from the bins, and other animals – mice, hedgehogs, badgers. You are not afraid of meeting any of these animals. You're a cat.

Your paws are sensitive, so you can feel the ground as you walk along. Maybe you're walking on paving slabs, which are still warm from the day. Reach a patch of cool grass and enjoy feeling the damp under your pads.

You smell another cat, and decide that you want to show it that you're the boss. There is a tree nearby. Jump at the tree with your strong back legs, and cling to the trunk with your sharp claws. You can easily climb up the tree trunk to a wide branch, because you're such an agile cat.

The other cat looks up at you, and you both decide that tonight, you are friends, and can't be bothered to argue.

Stretch out along your tree branch. Look up at the stars, putting on a glorious show of sparkly patterns for you to enjoy. One of the patterns, or constellations, is called Leo, named after a lion. A lion is a big cat, and Leo looks like he's lifting up a paw ready to bash something.

Your tree branch is wide and comfortable. You hear a deep, rumbling noise and realise that you are purring with happiness. Your breathing is slow and relaxed, and you can simply lie on your branch, stretching yourself out every now and then, satisfied that you are a cat.

ഇൻ

ABOUT THE AUTHOR

Maria Oliver is a Hertfordshire based yoga teacher and member of the British Wheel of Yoga.
She teaches general Hatha yoga as well as specialising in pregnancy,
postnatal and children's yoga.
Maria is passionate about sharing the mental and physical benefits of yoga and mindfulness and
making them accessible to everyone.
Her book *Once Upon a Time, You…* has been translated into French and Ukrainian.
In July 2022, 200 copies in English and Ukrainian were sent to refugee children all over the
United Kingdom, thanks to a Crowdfunder campaign.
She is married with two children and two cats, and this is her fourth book.
www.boxmooryoga.co.uk
Facebook, Instagram, Twitter: @boxmooryoga

ABOUT THE ILLUSTRATORS

Benjamin and Stephanie Grandis are Hertfordshire based illustrators, offering quirky and
humorous bespoke prints, illustrations and stationery.
They began working together during Lockdown in March 2020, bringing their unique visual
perspectives to every project they collaborate on.
They live with their son and dog, and this is the third book they have illustrated together.
harperprints.uk
Facebook: @harper.prints
Instagram: @harper.prints and @bharleyillustrations

MORE BOOKS BY MARIA OLIVER!

Red Kites, Apples and Blood Cells: Imaginative Relaxations for Lively Kids

Illustrated by Ben and Steph Grandis
Lie back and let yourself be transported... these imaginative relaxation scripts will help you and your child relax, switch off from everyday worries, and learn the art of being still. These adventures in relaxation can be used at the end of a yoga class, before bedtime, or any time when some calm is needed. Also available as an eBook on Kindle, or Audiobook on Amazon, iTunes and Audible.

Goldfinches, Daffodils and Sunshine: More Imaginative Relaxations for Lively Kids

Illustrated by Ben and Steph Grandis
Maria's second book of adventures in relaxation will help to slow down the body, mind and breath. Fly with a dragon, swim beneath the sea and let worries melt away like gooey chocolate. Perfect to help children of any age (and their grown-ups) to create their own inner calm. Also on Kindle.

Once Upon a Time, You... A Yoga / Chair Yoga Adventure where you choose what happens!

Who do you want to fly with, and where do you want to fly? Use yoga poses to help a golden eagle, a flying horse or a dragon on a special adventure where you choose what happens! Also on Kindle.